DOGS DON'T WEAR SNEAKERS

DOGS DON'T WEAR SNEAKERS

BY LAURA NUMEROFF

ILLUSTRATED BY JOE MATHIEU

SCHOLASTIC INC.

New York Toronto London Auckland Sydney

ISBN 0-590-60742-1

Text copyright © 1993 by Laura Numeroff.
Illustrations copyright © 1993 by Joe Mathieu.
All rights reserved. Published by Scholastic Inc., 555 Broadway, New York, NY 10012,
by arrangement with Simon & Schuster Books for Young Readers,
a division of Simon & Schuster.

12 11 10 9 8 7 6 5 4 3 2 1   5 6 7 8 9/9 0/0

Printed in U.S.A.   09

First Scholastic printing, January 1995

Dogs don't wear sneakers

And pigs don't wear hats

And dresses look silly
On Siamese cats.

Sheep don't take showers
And goats never shave

And you won't find a bathtub
Inside a bear's cave.

Moose don't go bowling

And hens never swim

And you'll never see roosters
Working out in a gym.

Skunks don't ride scooters

And beavers don't skate

And frogs don't take cabs
When they're out on a date.

Cows don't go dancing

And yaks never ski

And you won't find a honey bun
Baked by a bee.

Fish don't eat bagels

And penguins don't teach

And rabbits don't sunbathe
At your local beach.

Now just close your eyes
And draw with your mind.
You might be surprised
At what you will find...

Like parrots in tutus

And lambs selling shoes

And two-story houses
Constructed by gnus,

Or mules painting pictures

And ducks riding bikes

And raccoons with knapsacks
On holiday hikes,

Or bulls flying airplanes

And snails saving twine.